COMPREHENSION NINJA WORKBOOK

AGES 9–10

ANDREW JENNINGS

BLOOMSBURY EDUCATION

LONDON OXFORD NEW YORK NEW DELHI SYDNEY

BLOOMSBURY EDUCATION
Bloomsbury Publishing Plc
50 Bedford Square, London, WC1B 3DP, UK
29 Earlsfort Terrace, Dublin 2, Ireland

BLOOMSBURY, BLOOMSBURY EDUCATION and the Diana logo are trademarks of
Bloomsbury Publishing Plc

First published in Great Britain, 2020 by Bloomsbury Publishing Plc
Text copyright © Andrew Jennings, 2020

Ninja illustrations copyright © Andrew Jennings, 2020
Illustrations copyright pages 18, 27, 42 © Ilias Arahovitis, 2020
Illustrations copyright pages 5, 35 © Daniel Limon, 2020

Andrew Jennings has asserted his right under the Copyright, Designs and Patents Act, 1988,
to be identified as Author of this work

A catalogue record for this book is available from the British Library

ISBN: PB: 978-1-4729-8510-1; ePDF: 978-1-4729-8511-8

4 6 8 10 9 7 5 3

Text design by Marcus Duck Design

Printed and bound in the UK by Ashford Colour Press

To find out more about our authors and books visit www.bloomsbury.com and sign up for
our newsletters

Acknowledgements

To Christopher Hole, thank you for the inexhaustible level of quality you have brought to the
Comprehension Ninja series and beyond. Your subject knowledge, skills and experience have
been essential in developing the highest quality non-fiction texts, that are engaging, inspiring
and informative for the reader.

INTRODUCTION

Reading comprehension is all about understanding what you are reading – and being able to show that you understand. This Comprehension Ninja workbook will help your child master the foundations of reading comprehension by focusing on three key aspects:

- **Skimming** and **scanning** a whole text to locate information efficiently.
- **Retrieving** the correct information from the text in eight different ways.
- **Vocabulary** awareness and the **effect of word choices.**

This book contains seven curriculum-linked texts, each followed by a set of questions to check whether your child has understood the text. There are eight question types to develop your child's comprehension skills:

 Labelling   Matching    Fill in the gap    Multiple choice

 True or false    Find and copy    Sequencing    Underline or highlight

For texts 1 - 4, the activity pages feature one question type per page so your child can focus on building up their comprehension skills one at a time, while texts 5 - 7 look a bit more like a test, with two pages of mixed questions.
This book includes the following topics: fair trade, European culture, the Solar system, the British Empire, Australia and Banksy.

HOW TO USE THIS WORKBOOK

STEP 1 – READ THE TEXT CAREFULLY

Encourage your child to read the whole text carefully before they start trying to answer the questions. You can help them with any words or phrases they don't know. As an extra activity, you could ask your child to read the text aloud to you.

STEP 2 – PICK OUT KEY WORDS AND INFORMATION

Picking out key words and headings will help your child to quickly locate the information they need to answer the questions. Encourage your child to underline key information as they read the text, such as:

- **Nouns** – names of people, places and objects.
- **Time** – dates and periods of time.
- **Numbers** – amounts, statistics, percentages and figures.
- **Vocabulary** – important topic vocabulary or words they are unsure of. They could look these up online or in a dictionary to find out what they mean.

Your child should also look out for titles and headings, which will help them understand the structure of the text.

STEP 3 – IDENTIFY KEY WORDS IN THE QUESTIONS

Encourage your child to identify key words in the questions so they know what they're looking for to find the answer. For example, in a text about the seaside:

> **Question**: What might you find in a rock pool?

> **Key words**: rock pool

'Rock pool' is the clue needed to answer the question.

STEP 4 – SKIM AND SCAN THE TEXT

Once your child has identified the key words in the question, they can try to remember where in the text the answer can be found. This might be as simple as remembering whether it was at the beginning, middle or end of the text, or thinking about which section the key information was in.

Your child can then **skim read** the whole text to find the section they need. When they've found it, they should **scan** the section to find the relevant sentences. They then read those sentences carefully to find the answer.

Invite your child to work through all the questions and give them lots of encouragement along the way. The answers can be found at the back of the book.

1 FAIR TRADE

What is fair trade?

To understand the meaning of fair trade, we can look at each word: 'fair' means 'equal and without discrimination' and 'trade' is the action of buying and selling goods. By putting them together, we can begin to understand that fair trade is about ensuring everyone in the world is treated in the same way when it comes to buying and selling goods. Unfortunately, this isn't always the case.

Why do we need to address fair trade?

Fair trade focuses on producers in 'developing' countries: countries with economies that are weaker than average and have a high need to sell their products. Historically, farmers in developing countries haven't been paid the same as those in developed countries.

As a consequence, farmers don't always make enough money to live – even though they have worked day and night to produce a high-quality product. Large companies exploit farmers' and workers' need to sell, making a huge profit and passing none of it to their suppliers.

What does fair trade achieve?

The fair trade movement aims to ensure that producers are paid a price that is never below the world value of their product. This should allow producers to keep their businesses running.

In this way, fair trade aims to enable even the poorest farmers to feed their families, drink clean water, clothe their children and buy medicines when needed. This may allow them to develop their businesses and their communities, too.

As of 2019, more than 1.66 million farmers and workers are fair trade certified, and there are 1,411 certified producers in 73 countries across the world. In 2016, $158.3 million was paid to these fair trade producers.

The fair trade of coffee

One of the fair trade movement's priorities is the trade of coffee. Coffee is one of the world's most popular drinks, and its sale is extremely profitable. The cost of producing it is low, and the price of coffee to customers is high.

Coffee is made from small beans that are roasted and ground down into a powder or granules. The beans are actually berries – they come from trees called 'coffea'. It's only after they're dried that they're called beans.

The origins of coffee can be traced back centuries to ancient coffea forests in Ethiopia. Legend says the goat herder Kaldi first discovered their potential after noticing that his goats became energetic after eating coffea berries. Monasteries started making them into a drink that kept the monks alert during evening prayer. From there, word moved east and coffee became popular across the globe.

Nearly all of the world's coffee is now grown in a region called the 'coffee belt', which is close to the equator. It includes India and Indonesia, and much of Africa and South America. Soil there is rich in nutrients, and the climate is warm and wet – perfect for growing coffea plants. Many countries in the coffee belt are classed as 'developing' countries.

Nowadays, small farms produce 80 per cent of the world's coffee, and it's estimated that 125 million people rely on the coffee trade for their livelihoods. Without the simple coffee bean, millions of people would be without work.

How can we support fair trade?

The most important thing you and your family can do is to buy fair trade products. Keep an eye out for the Fairtrade Foundation's circular green, black and blue logo on packaging. It can be seen on lots of products, including coffee. This logo informs the consumer that the producer of the product is guaranteed to receive a fair price.

✏ FILL IN THE GAP

Read the sentences and choose the correct word or words to fill the gap.

To understand the meaning of fair trade, we can look at each word: 'fair' means 'equal and without _____' and 'trade' is the action of buying and selling goods.

By putting them together, we can begin to understand that fair trade is about ensuring everyone in the world is _____ in the same way when it comes to buying and selling goods.

Fair trade focuses on producers in '_____' countries.

As a _____, farmers don't always make enough money to live – even though they have worked day and night to produce a high-quality product.

Large companies _____ farmers' and workers' need to sell, making a huge profit and passing none of it to their suppliers.

The fair trade movement aims to ensure that _____ are paid a price that is never below the world value of their product.

This should allow producers to keep their _____ running.

In this way, fair trade aims to enable even the poorest farmers to feed their families, drink _____ water, clothe their children and buy medicines when needed.

The beans are actually berries – they come from trees called '_____'.

Legend says the goat herder _____ first discovered their potential after noticing that his goats became energetic after eating coffea berries.

_____ started making them into a drink that kept the monks alert during evening prayer.

Soil there is rich in nutrients, and the _____ is warm and wet.

Nowadays, small farms produce _____ of the world's coffee.

Without the simple coffee bean, _____ of people would be without work.

The most important thing you and your family can do is to buy _____ products.

 MATCHING

Draw a line with a ruler to match the information.

fair trade focuses on	Kaldi
number of certified producers	'developing' countries
goat herder	coffee belt
close to the equator	1,411

farmers don't have enough	exploit farmers
large companies	the coffee belt
coffee growing region	everyone treated the same
fair trade ensures	money

paid to fair trade producers	guarantee the producer has been paid a fair price
Fairtrade Foundation logo	a tree
coffee	a very popular drink
coffea	$158.3 million

trade means	equal and without discrimination
Fairtrade Foundation logo	73
fair means	buying and selling goods
fair trade countries	green, black and blue

1.66 million	coffea berries
energetic goats ate	clothes, food and medicines
small farms produce	fair trade certified farmers and workers
farmers use money for	80 per cent of the world's coffee

◉ MULTIPLE CHOICE

Circle the correct answer for each of the following questions.

What does the word 'fair' mean?

| everyone is equal | everyone is different | everyone is treated the same | everyone knows the same |

What does the word 'trade' mean?

| buying and selling goods | a market | the same products | giving away your product |

Where is most coffee produced?

| India, Indonesia, Africa and South America | Japan | London, England | North America |

What is coffee made from?

| a cactus | a flower | an animal | a berry |

Before fair trade, farmers were being…

| harmed | exploited | cared for | bullied |

Fair trade was introduced to ensure profits were shared with…

| producers | sellers | large companies | investors |

What are coffee beans turned into?

| liquid | berries | powder or granules | tea |

What is the name of the plant that produces coffee?

| coffea | coffee | cofea | cofee |

What is the name of the region that produces most of the world's coffee?

| the coffee centre | the coffee equator | the coffee lands | the coffee belt |

What shape is the Fairtrade Foundation's logo?

| a square | a triangle | a hexagon | a circle |

1 FAIR TRADE

👍 TRUE OR FALSE

Read the sentences. Put a tick in the correct box to show which sentences are *true* and which are *false*.

Fair means to be treated equally.　　　　　　　True ☐　False ☐

Trade means the action of buying and selling.　　True ☐　False ☐

It is always the case that people are treated in the same way.　True ☐　False ☐

Poor and rich countries' farmers will be paid the same.　True ☐　False ☐

Fair trade focuses on producers in 'developed' countries.　True ☐　False ☐

Fair trade protects farmers from being exploited.　True ☐　False ☐

Fair trade aims to help even the poorest farmers.　True ☐　False ☐

Large companies pass their profits on to their supplier.　True ☐　False ☐

Fair trade allows farmers to feed and clothe their families.　True ☐　False ☐

Fair trade allows farmers to sell their businesses.　True ☐　False ☐

Coffee is one of the world's most popular drinks.　True ☐　False ☐

Coffee is produced from a leaf.　　　　　　　True ☐　False ☐

Coffee comes from a tree called coffea.　　　　True ☐　False ☐

Nearly all of the world's coffee is grown in factories.　True ☐　False ☐

The coffee belt is close to the equator.　　　　True ☐　False ☐

Coffee became popular across the globe when word moved west.　True ☐　False ☐

Small farms produce 100 per cent of the world's coffee.　True ☐　False ☐

Monasteries made a drink with the berries of the coffea tree.　True ☐　False ☐

Kodi the cow herder discovered the coffee bean.　True ☐　False ☐

The Fairtrade Foundation logo is on all products.　True ☐　False ☐

Europe isn't a country but a continent. There are seven continents on Earth and each is divided into countries. Europe contains over 40 different countries, all of which have their own histories, traditions and cultures. France, Ukraine, Poland, Hungary, Norway and Spain are some of the countries in Europe.

Each individual country's culture is deeply rooted in different forms of art, architecture, literature, music, sport and even behaviour. Cultures have developed differently throughout Europe, while sharing some common themes.

Let's look at just a few of them.

German culture

German is the official language of Germany. Many other native languages are spoken too though, such as Polish, Kurdish and Danish, which shows how multi-cultural the country is. Many German classical musicians are world-famous, having composed some of the most recognisable concertos and symphonies in history. They include the composers Ludwig van Beethoven, Richard Wagner, Richard Strauss and Johann Sebastian Bach.

Sport in Germany is hugely important, too. The German men's football team has been ever-present in major competitions: they won World Cups in 1954, 1974, 1990 and 2014, and European Championships in 1972, 1980 and 1996. In motor sports, Michael Schumacher and Sebastian Vettel have also won 11 Formula 1 World Championships between them.

Some of Germany's most famous exported foods are its delicious sausages: bratwurst, currywurst, bockwurst – and many more! Germany is also world-famous for its beer. Both sausages and beer are celebrated at its annual festival, Oktoberfest.

Danish culture

When you hear 'Denmark', you may think immediately of Vikings: fierce warriors who savagely invaded and raided other countries. However, Denmark nowadays has a strong culture promoting the arts and intellectual pursuits. Theatre, music, sculpture, photography and film receive large amounts of government funding in comparison to other countries. Involvement in the arts is believed to have a great positive impact on people's happiness.

Cycling also plays a major role in many Danes' lives. In many cities, cycle lanes are clear and wide, meaning people can cycle as a mode of transport, cycle for fun and train to cycle competitively for teams. Over 1.3 million people cycle in the city of Copenhagen each day, while Odense was named 'bicycle city of the year' for its 350-kilometre network of cycle lanes.

Greek culture

When you think of Greece, you might think of its ancient legends: perhaps of Zeus, the king of the gods; Poseidon, god of the seas; and Hades, god of the underworld. Perhaps you think about the stories of the Trojan War, Theseus and the Minotaur, or Cerberus, the three-headed dog who guarded the gates of hell. Greek culture certainly remembers its mythical past, but strongly embraces the present.

Greece holds the record for the most gold medals won at the Olympics per person in the population, and its basketball team is successful: they even beat the USA's 'dream team' in the 2006 World Cup.

Greece is also famous for its cuisine. Fresh fish from the Mediterranean sea, sun-ripened vegetables, creamy feta cheese and lashings of olive oil also make it one of the healthiest in the world.

Symbols of culture

European culture is recognised around the world and is symbolised by some historic, iconic buildings. The Colosseum in Rome, Italy, symbolises military and theatrical prowess. The Louvre Museum, in Paris, France, embodies the French love of art and all things beautiful. The Parthenon, in Greece, illustrates the country's respect for its ancient culture and gods. In London, United Kingdom, the Houses of Parliament and Buckingham Palace represent democracy and the royal family.

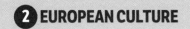

Read the sentences and choose the correct word or words to fill the gap.

Europe isn't a country but a _____.

Europe contains over 40 different countries, all of which have their own histories, _____ and cultures.

Each individual country's culture is deeply rooted in different forms of art, _____, literature, music, sport and even behaviour.

Many other native languages are spoken too though, such as Polish, _____ and Danish, which shows how multi-cultural the country is.

Many German _____ are world-famous, having composed some of the most recognisable concertos and symphonies in history.

They include the composers _____, Richard Wagner, Richard Strauss and Johann Sebastian Bach.

_____ in Germany is hugely important, too.

Germany is also _____ for its beer.

When you hear 'Denmark', you may think immediately of _____: fierce warriors who savagely invaded and raided other countries.

Theatre, music, sculpture, photography and film receive large amounts of _____ funding in comparison to other countries.

Cycling also plays a major role in many _____ lives.

Greek culture certainly remembers its _____ past, but strongly embraces the present.

Greece is also famous for its cuisine. Fresh fish from the Mediterranean sea, _____ vegetables, creamy feta cheese and lashings of olive oil also make it one of the healthiest in the world.

The _____ in Rome, Italy, symbolises military and theatrical prowess.

 **MATCHING**

Draw a line with a ruler to match the information.

German culture	Zeus and Hades
Danish culture	a continent
Greek culture	Polish, Kurdish and Danish languages
Europe	Viking links

Greek culture	arts, theatre and culture
Danish culture	Greece
German culture	Trojan War
the Parthenon	classical musicians

olive oil	German culture
cycling	London
motor sports	Danish culture
Houses of Parliament	Greek culture

Danish culture	the Colosseum, Rome
Greek culture	Beethoven and Bach
German culture	Mediterranean sea
symbol of culture	government funding for the arts

Theseus	London
Paris	sausages
royal family	the Louvre
exported food	Minotaur

◎ MULTIPLE CHOICE

Circle the correct answer for each of the following questions.

How many countries are there in Europe?

| over 30 | over 40 | over 50 | over 60 |

When did the German men's football team first win the World Cup?

| 1947 | 1954 | 2014 | 1958 |

Which culture traditionally eats currywurst?

| Danish | Scottish | German | Greek |

Which culture believes in the positive impact of the arts?

| Greek | German | Italian | Danish |

How many Formula 1 titles have been won by Schumacher and Vettel?

| 11 | 12 | 13 | 14 |

The Greek basketball team beat which other nation's team in the 2006 World Cup?

| Italy | USA | Germany | France |

Which of the following is a symbol of military prowess?

| Louvre Museum | Houses of Parliament | Colosseum | Parthenon |

Which culture is famous for its use of olive oil?

| Greek | German | Norwegian | Danish |

Which culture places a lot of importance on cycling?

| Greek | German | Norwegian | Danish |

Which culture is known for its famous classical musicians?

| Greek | German | Italian | Danish |

 # TRUE OR FALSE

Read the sentences. Put a tick in the correct box to show which sentences are _true_ and which are _false_.

There are over 50 countries in Europe.　　　　　　　　True ☐　False ☐

Hungary is a country found in Europe.　　　　　　　　True ☐　False ☐

Europe is a country.　　　　　　　　True ☐　False ☐

Ukraine is a country found in Europe.　　　　　　　　True ☐　False ☐

Kurdish is spoken in Germany.　　　　　　　　True ☐　False ☐

Michael Schumacher is from Denmark.　　　　　　　　True ☐　False ☐

Over 2 million people cycle in Copenhagen each day.　　　　　　　　True ☐　False ☐

Polish is spoken in Germany.　　　　　　　　True ☐　False ☐

Germany has many famous classical musicians.　　　　　　　　True ☐　False ☐

The Parthenon is in Paris.　　　　　　　　True ☐　False ☐

The Houses of Parliament are in Odense.　　　　　　　　True ☐　False ☐

The Colosseum is in Rome.　　　　　　　　True ☐　False ☐

Odense is a city in Denmark.　　　　　　　　True ☐　False ☐

A bratwurst is a type of bicycle.　　　　　　　　True ☐　False ☐

Danish citizens are heavily involved in the arts.　　　　　　　　True ☐　False ☐

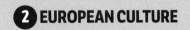

FIND AND COPY

These questions are about *European culture*.

Look at paragraph one. Find and copy a word that suggests that continents are made up of more than one country.

_____

Look at the 'German culture' section. Find and copy a word that suggests the music that classical musicians wrote was familiar and well-known.

_____

Look at the 'German culture' section. Find and copy a word that suggests that musicians wrote music.

_____

Look at the 'German culture' section. Find and copy a word that suggests that German food is eaten in lots of other countries.

_____

Look at the 'German culture' section. Find and copy a word that suggests that Oktoberfest happens every year.

_____

Look at the 'Danish culture' section. Find and copy a word that suggests that the Vikings took things from other places.

_____

Look at the 'Greek culture' section. Find and copy a word that suggests that Cerberus protected hell.

_____

Look at the 'Symbols of culture' section. Find and copy a word that suggests that the Parthenon shows others about Greece's respect for the gods.

_____

✎ UNDERLINE OR HIGHLIGHT

Read the paragraphs below and then follow the instructions.

German is the official language of Germany. Many other native languages are spoken too though, such as Polish, Kurdish and Danish, representing how multi-cultural the country is. Many German classical musicians are world-famous, having composed some of the most recognisable concertos and symphonies in history. They include the composers Ludwig van Beethoven, Richard Wagner, Richard Strauss and Johann Sebastian Bach.

Sport in Germany is hugely important, too. The German men's football team has been ever-present in major competitions: they won World Cups in 1954, 1974, 1990 and 2014, and European Championships in 1972, 1980 and 1996. In motor sports, Michael Schumacher and Sebastian Vettel have also won 11 Formula 1 World Championships between them.

Some of Germany's most famously exported foods are its delicious sausages: bratwurst, currywurst, bockwurst – and many more! Germany is also world-famous for its beer. Both sausages and beer are celebrated at its annual festival, Oktoberfest.

Underline or highlight a word that means approved by a country's government.

Underline or highlight a word that means a very pleasant taste.

Underline or highlight a word that means honoured and marked publicly.

Underline or highlight a word that means linked to a particular place..

Underline or highlight a word that means sold to other countries.

Underline or highlight a word that means someone who plays an instrument as a hobby or job.

3 PLANETS IN THE SOLAR SYSTEM

A solar system is a sun and the planets that move around it. Our Solar system contains eight planets. Not all have been explored fully, but scientists and experts have managed to piece together a range of facts to help us understand them.

Mercury

Mercury is the smallest planet in the Solar system, only a little bigger than Earth's moon. It is the closest to the Sun but not the hottest – and it's still a staggering 57 million kilometres away. It takes around 88 Earth days to complete a round journey or 'orbit' around the Sun (which takes Earth a year). This is the shortest time of any planet in the Solar system. However one full rotation (which is how we measure a day on Earth) lasts almost 59 Earth days.

Venus

Venus has extreme temperatures and acidic clouds, which make the existence of life there unlikely. It is the hottest of the planets, with a surface temperature of around 460°C. A year for Venus takes 224.7 Earth days, and a day lasts almost the same amount of time: 243 Earth days. Unusually, Venus's rotation is in the opposite direction to Earth's.

Earth

The fifth largest planet in the Solar system, our planet is the only one we know is inhabited by living things and the only one we know has liquid water. Earth is around 150 million kilometres from the Sun and takes 365 days to orbit it.

Mars

Mars is home to polar ice caps, extinct volcanoes and canyons. This planet – the fourth from the Sun – is well explored by humans. A day on Mars lasts just over 24 hours and it takes the planet 687 Earth days to orbit the Sun. It is known as the 'red planet' due to the rusty fragments of iron in its soil.

Jupiter

By far the largest planet in the Solar system, Jupiter is twice as big as all of the other planets combined. It has 79 moons. A day lasts about ten Earth hours but a year takes about 12 Earth years. Jupiter is made mostly of hydrogen and helium: it does not have a solid surface, so spacecraft would be unable to land. Its extreme pressures and temperatures would also destroy any vehicle.

Saturn

Similar to Jupiter, Saturn is mainly made up of hydrogen and helium. Perhaps its most famous feature is its many rings, which are made of ice and rock. Saturn is believed to have a total of 62 moons. Although Saturn itself cannot support life similar to that on Earth, some of its moons are believed to have conditions that may support it. A year on Saturn lasts around 29.5 Earth years, and a day lasts almost 11 hours.

Uranus

Uranus is four times wider than Earth. It takes about 84 Earth years to complete a full orbit of the Sun, and about 17 hours to rotate once. Similar to Venus, Uranus's rotation is in a direction opposite to that of most planets. Uniquely, Uranus rotates on its side.

Neptune

Almost 30 times as far away from the Sun as Earth is, Neptune is the most distant planet in the Solar system. Neptune, which was not discovered until 1846, is not visible to the naked eye from Earth. It takes about 16 Earth hours to rotate once, but around 165 Earth years to orbit the Sun, meaning it has so far completed only one rotation since its discovery. It has 13 moons and six known rings. Due to its icy properties, it would not be able to support life as we know it.

✏ FILL IN THE GAP

Read the sentences and choose the correct word or words to fill the gap.

Our Solar system contains _____ planets.

Not all have been _____ fully, but scientists and experts have managed to piece together a range of facts to help us understand them.

Mercury is the smallest planet in the Solar system, only a little bigger than Earth's _____.

It is the _____ to the Sun, but not the hottest – and it's still a staggering 57 million kilometres away.

Venus has extreme temperatures and _____ clouds, which make the existence of life there unlikely.

Unusually, Venus's rotation is in the _____ direction to Earth's.

A day on Mars lasts just over 24 hours and it takes the planet 687 Earth days to _____ the Sun.

It is known as the 'red planet' due to the rusty fragments of _____ in its soil.

A day lasts about _____ Earth hours, but a year takes about 12 Earth years.

Jupiter is made mostly of hydrogen and helium: it does not have a solid surface, so _____ would be unable to land.

Saturn is believed to have a total of _____ moons.

It takes about 84 Earth years to complete a full orbit of _____, and about 17 hours to rotate once.

Almost 30 times as far away from the Sun as Earth is, _____ is the most distant planet in the Solar system.

It takes about 16 Earth hours to rotate once, but around 165 Earth years to orbit the Sun, meaning it has so far completed only one rotation since its _____.

Due to its icy _____, it would not be able to support life as we know it.

MATCHING

Draw a line with a ruler to match the information.

Mercury	iron
Earth	hydrogen and helium
Mars	closest to the Sun
Saturn	fifth largest planet

Venus	four times wider than Earth
Jupiter	hottest planet
Uranus	not visible to the naked eye
Neptune	largest planet in the solar system

discovered in 1846	Jupiter
red planet	Mars
79 moons in total	Saturn
62 moons in total	Neptune

destroy any vehicle	Neptune
165 years to orbit the Sun	Venus
smallest planet	Jupiter
rotation is opposite direction to Earth	Mercury

Earth	eight planets
Solar system	rings of ice and rock
Mercury	88 Earth days to orbit the Sun
Saturn	365 days to orbit the Sun

 LABEL

Label the information with the correct planet.

closest planet to the sun	
the largest planet in the solar system	
has polar ice caps, extinct volcanoes and canyons	
made up of hydrogen and helium	
most distant planet in the solar system	
four times wider than Earth	

Label the information with the correct planet.

takes 84 years to orbit the Sun	
62 moons	
takes 687 Earth days to orbit the Sun	
has liquid water	
called the 'red planet'	
some moons could support life	

Label the information with the correct planet.

has 79 moons	
rotates in the opposite direction to Earth	
has 13 moons	
discovered in 1846	
rotates on its side	
rings made of ice and rock	

123 SEQUENCING

Look at *Planets in the solar system*. Number the statements from 1 to 5 to show the order they occur in the text. Look at the first line of each paragraph to help you.

The fifth largest planet in the Solar system, our planet is the only one we know is inhabited by living things and the only one we know has liquid water. ☐

By far the largest planet in the solar system, Jupiter is twice as big as all of the other planets combined. ☐

Similar to Jupiter, Saturn is mainly made up of hydrogen and helium. ☐

Mercury is the smallest planet in the Solar system, only a little bigger than Earth's moon. ☐

Almost 30 times as far away from the Sun as Earth is, Neptune is the most distant planet in the Solar system. ☐

Look at the 'Saturn' section in *Planets in the solar system*. Number the statements from 1 to 5 to show the order they occur in the text.

A year on Saturn lasts around 29.5 Earth years, and a day lasts almost 11 hours. ☐

Similar to Jupiter, Saturn is mainly made up of hydrogen and helium. ☐

Although Saturn itself cannot support life similar to that on Earth, some of its moons are believed to have conditions that may support it. ☐

Saturn is believed to have a total of 62 moons. ☐

Perhaps its most famous feature is its many rings, which are made of ice and rock. ☐

Look at *Planets in the solar system*. Number the statements from 1 to 5 to show the order they occur in the text.

However one full rotation (which is how we measure a day on Earth) lasts almost 59 Earth days. ☐

A year on Saturn lasts around 29.5 Earth years, and a day lasts almost 11 hours. ☐

Earth is around 150 million kilometres from the Sun and takes 365 days to orbit it. ☐

A year for Venus takes 224.7 Earth days, and a day lasts almost the same amount of time: 243 Earth days. ☐

Jupiter is made mostly of hydrogen and helium: it does not have a solid surface, so spacecraft would be unable to land. ☐

 FIND AND COPY

These questions are about *Planets in the solar system*.

Look at paragraph one. Find and copy two words that suggest that some of the world's most knowledgeable people are involved in space exploration.

_____

Look at the 'Mercury' section. Find and copy a word that suggests that Mercury is turning all the time.

_____

Look at the 'Venus' section. Find and copy a word that suggests that there is something odd about how Venus rotates.

_____

Look at the 'Earth' section. Find and copy a word that suggests that there are living things on Earth.

_____

Look at the 'Mars' section. Find and copy a word that suggests that Mars's volcanoes are no longer active or erupting.

_____

Look at the 'Saturn' section. Find and copy a word that suggests that Saturn is very much like Jupiter.

_____

Look at the 'Uranus' section. Find and copy a word that suggests that Uranus does something that no other planet does.

_____

Look at the 'Neptune' section. Find and copy a word that suggests that Neptune has icy features.

_____

✎UNDERLINE OR HIGHLIGHT

Read the paragraphs below and then follow the instructions.

Saturn

Similar to Jupiter, Saturn is mainly made up of hydrogen and helium. Perhaps its most famous feature is its many rings, which are made of ice and rock. Saturn is believed to have a total of 62 moons. Although Saturn itself cannot support life similar to that on Earth, some of its moons are believed to have conditions that may support it. A year on Saturn lasts around 29.5 Earth years, and a day lasts almost 11 hours.

Neptune

Almost 30 times as far away from the Sun as Earth is, Neptune is the most distant planet in the Solar system. Neptune, which was not discovered until 1846, is not visible to the naked eye from Earth. It takes about 16 Earth hours to rotate once, but around 165 Earth years to orbit the Sun, meaning it has so far completed only one rotation since its discovery. It has 13 moons and six known rings. Due to its icy properties, it would not be able to support life as we know it.

Underline or highlight a word that means an interesting part of something.

Underline or highlight a word that means to finish something.

Underline or highlight a word that means very far away.

Underline or highlight a word that means to enable something to live.

Underline or highlight a word that means something is thought to be true.

Underline or highlight a word that means to turn in a circular movement.

4 MENTAL HEALTH

What is mental health?

In the same way that physical health is about the body, mental health is about the mind.

Someone's mental health is the measure of how they think and feel. Good mental health suggests that people can think clearly and cope well with their emotional states. It also suggests that they are aware of the way they behave and can usually control it. Many people believe that mental health is also a measure of happiness.

The 21st century has seen a significant rise in mental health problems being reported, especially by young people.

What are mental health problems?

Mental health problems can affect anyone, at any stage of their life – and, more often than not, they creep up on people. They can significantly affect people's moods and actions before people realise it.

Mental health problems can be inherited and they can be the result of a physical health problem. Many arise as a result of stress or emotional trauma such as a death, repeated abuse or an experience of violence. In 2018, one survey found that 74 per cent of people went through periods when they felt so stressed they were overwhelmed or unable to cope.

It is also believed that lifestyle factors such as diet, levels of exercise and social encounters can affect a person's mental health.

What defines a mental health disorder?

Many of the feelings associated with mental health disorders also occur commonly and naturally. For example, you may feel nervous before a test – but tests are logical causes for worry. When thoughts or feelings become a persistent problem they may be related to a mental health disorder.

The following are just a few of the many mental health problems that affect people.

Anxiety is a feeling of intense or prolonged fear or panic. In 2013, there were 8.2 million reported cases of anxiety in the UK. One in six young people reported experiencing it.

Anorexia and bulimia are eating disorders. Sufferers tend to worry about their weight to an unhealthy extent and persist in trying to lose weight. Girls are ten times more likely than boys to develop eating disorders.

Depression is a condition defined by extremely low mood and can also cause people to avoid activity. Depression is one of the most common mental health disorders reported.

Obsessive-compulsive disorder (OCD) can trigger relentlessly repeating thoughts, images or feelings. Sufferers may repeat actions over and over, for example washing their hands.

Who can help with mental health problems?

Treatment is available for the mind, just like for the body. If you have questions or concerns about your mental health, some advice is available online from charities such as Mind. However, the first and most important step to take is to speak to someone you trust. You should then contact your regular or local doctor. Doctors have access to specialist mental health services and can refer patients so they receive the most suitable help.

How can we improve our mental health?

We should take care of our mental health as much as our physical health. There are many simple things that can be done to boost mental wellbeing.

- Make time for friendships. Shared experiences stop people feeling isolated and alone.

- Exercising your body will help your mind. Exercising releases natural 'happy' chemicals called endorphins. Endorphins fight stress and can relieve depression.

- Get out into nature. Fresh air, vitamin D from the sun and gentle exercise are all proven to lift moods. Even plants and animals in people's homes can help.

- Talk about your mental health. Many people, especially boys and men, are taught that discussing feelings is a sign of weakness. The opposite is true.

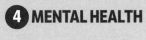

LABEL

Label the description with the correct condition(s).

a feeling of fear or panic	
repeating thoughts, images or feelings	
feeling extremely low	
an eating disorder	
one in six young people experience it	
worry about weight	

Label the description with the correct information.

percentage of people who felt stressed in 2018	
'happy' chemicals	
mental health charity	
activity that releases 'happy' chemicals	
vitamin that the sun can provide	
having these in your home can improve wellbeing	

Label the description with the correct condition(s).

8.2 million cases across the UK	
result of emotional trauma	
relentlessly repeating thoughts	
girls ten times more likely to have this than boys	
one of the most common types of mental illness	
sufferers repeat actions over and over	

123 SEQUENCING

Look at *Mental health*. Number the statements from 1 to 5 to show the order they occur in the text. Look at the first line of each paragraph to help you.

Mental health problems can affect anyone, at any stage of their life – and, more often than not, they creep up on people.

Many of the feelings associated with mental health disorders also occur commonly and naturally.

Someone's mental health is the measure of how they think and feel.

Treatment is available for the mind, just like for the body.

We should take care of our mental health as much as our physical health.

Look at the 'What defines a mental health disorder?' section in *Mental health*. Number the statements from 1 to 5 to show the order they occur in the text.

Obsessive-compulsive disorder (OCD) can trigger relentlessly repeating thoughts, images or feelings.

When thoughts or feelings become a persistent problem they may be related to a mental health disorder.

Anxiety is a feeling of intense or prolonged fear or panic.

Anorexia and bulimia are eating disorders.

Depression is a condition defined by extremely low mood and can also cause people to avoid activity.

Look at *Mental health*. Number the statements from 1 to 5 to show the order they occur in the text.

Someone's mental health is the measure of how they think and feel.

Many people believe that mental health is also a measure of happiness.

When thoughts or feelings become a persistent problem, they may be related to a mental health disorder.

Endorphins fight stress and can relieve depression.

Many people, especially boys and men, are taught that discussing feelings is a sign of weakness.

◉ MULTIPLE CHOICE

Circle the correct answer for each of the following questions.

Which century has seen a significant rise in mental health problems being reported?

| 19th century | 20th century | 21st century | 22nd century |

Which of the following is a mental health problem that is characterised by an intense feeling of fear or panic?

| anxiety | anorexia | depression | bulimia |

Which of the following is a mental health problem that is characterised by extreme low mood?

| anorexia | depression | OCD | depression |

Which of the following is a mental health problem that is known as an eating disorder?

| anxiety | bulimia | OCD | depression |

In which year were 74 per cent of people stressed and unable to cope?

| 2016 | 2017 | 2018 | 2019 |

Who can direct you to specialist mental health services?

| nurses | teachers | parents | doctors |

Which of the following can help your body to release natural 'happy' chemicals?

| diet | exercise | massage | talking |

Where can you get vitamin D from?

| plants | exercise | sun | food |

Which of the following is a mental health charity?

| Heart | Health | Happy | Mind |

Which of the following is a mental health problem that is characterised by repeating thoughts?

| anxiety | bulimia | OCD | depression |

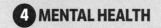 

TRUE OR FALSE

Read the sentences. Put a tick in the correct box to show which sentences are *true* and which are *false*.

Mental health is all about a person's emotional wellbeing.   True ☐   False ☐

Mental health affects how we feel and think.   True ☐   False ☐

The 21st century has seen a rise in reported mental health problems.   True ☐   False ☐

Mental health problems only affect adults.   True ☐   False ☐

Mental health problems are sometimes linked to stress.   True ☐   False ☐

In 2018, 47 per cent of people felt so stressed they couldn't cope.   True ☐   False ☐

Anxiety is an eating disorder.   True ☐   False ☐

Anorexia is ten times more likely to affect boys than girls.   True ☐   False ☐

Anxiety is a feeling of fear or panic.   True ☐   False ☐

One in six adults experience anxiety at some point.   True ☐   False ☐

Anorexia is a problem where you tend to worry about your weight.   True ☐   False ☐

There were 8.2 million cases of anxiety in 2013.   True ☐   False ☐

Depression is a very common mental illness.   True ☐   False ☐

Depression is where you have repeating thoughts.   True ☐   False ☐

People with OCD may repeat actions.   True ☐   False ☐

 FIND AND COPY

These questions are about _Mental health_.

Look at paragraph two. Find and copy a word that suggests how people deal well with their emotions.

_____

Look at paragraph three. Find and copy a word that suggests that the increase in mental health problems has been large.

_____

Look at 'What are mental health problems?'. Find and copy a word that suggests that people can receive mental health problems from their parents.

_____

Look at 'What are mental health problems?'. Find and copy a word that suggests some problems can make people feel like it is all too much to deal with.

_____

Look at 'What defines a mental health disorder?'. Find and copy a word that suggests that people may worry before a test.

_____

Look at 'What defines a mental health disorder?'. Find and copy a word that suggests that thoughts or feelings keep happening.

_____

Look at the paragraph beginning 'Depression'. Find and copy a word that suggests that depression might cause people to not want to exercise.

_____

Look at the paragraph beginning 'Obsessive-compulsive disorder'. Find and copy a word that suggests that some thoughts can feel like they will never stop happening.

_____

UNDERLINE OR HIGHLIGHT

Read the paragraphs below and then follow the instructions.

What defines a mental health disorder?

> Many of the feelings associated with mental health disorders also occur commonly and naturally. For example, you may feel nervous before a test – but tests are logical causes for worry. When thoughts or feelings become a persistent problem, they may be related to a mental health disorder.
>
> The following are just a few of the many mental health problems that affect people.
>
> Anxiety is a feeling of intense or prolonged fear or panic. In 2013, there were 8.2 million reported cases of anxiety in the UK. One in six young people reported experiencing it.
>
> Anorexia and bulimia are eating disorders. Sufferers tend to worry about their weight to an unhealthy extent and persist in trying to lose weight. Girls are ten times more likely than boys to develop eating disorders.
>
> Depression is a condition defined by extremely low mood and can also cause people to avoid activity. Depression is one of the most common mental health disorders reported.
>
> Obsessive-compulsive disorder (OCD) can trigger relentlessly repeating thoughts, images or feelings. Sufferers may repeat actions over and over, for example washing their hands.

Underline or highlight a word that means when things are connected with each other.

Underline or highlight a word that means to give information about something, often in a newspaper.

Underline or highlight a word that means something follows the rules of logic; it is sensible.

Underline or highlight a word that means a problem which affects mind or body.

Underline or highlight a word that means a very strong feeling of fear which makes you act without thinking.

Underline or highlight a word that means something continues to happen for a long time.

The British Empire was, at its greatest extent, the largest empire the world has ever seen. It covered over six times more land than the Roman Empire and included almost seven times as many people.

It began relatively late in empires' history. Throughout the 16th century, England had been envious of Portugal's and Spain's established overseas empires, which had created great wealth and fame for both countries in the Americas.

Between the late 16th and 18th centuries, Britain expanded its trade network across the world. New trade ports meant new settlements, or 'colonies'. In 1607, Britain planned to establish trading and stock companies to manage colonisation attempts in North America. They were created to sell the gold, sugar, furs and people being traded in and out of the Americas. England's first permanent settlement was founded.

In 1670, the lucrative Hudson's Bay Company was created in what is now Canada, to gather and trade in the fur of moose, beaver, squirrel and even otter. 1672 saw the founding of perhaps the most awful addition: the Royal African Company, which made money by taking slaves from Africa and selling them to British colonies in the Americas. Slavery was made illegal in Britain in 1807, but not across the Empire until 1834. By then, the Empire had transported over 3.5 million slaves across the Atlantic Ocean.

In total, 13 British colonies were established in North America – but by 1770 the relationship between the colonies and Britain had broken down. The 13 Colonies declared independence from Britain and formed the United States in 1776. Canada, however, remained loyal.

After losing control of the United States, Britain further explored Asia and Australia. In 1770, Captain James Cook claimed Australia for Britain. Colonies and farms were founded, but conditions were harsh. Seventeen years later, Britain decided to populate Australia by sending convicted British criminals to serve their sentences there. The amount of gold that they mined and the wool that they produced made Australia extremely profitable.

Asia was now Britain's next target. During the 1800s, the British East India Company, which specialised in the trade of tea, cotton, silk, salt and spices, was used to drive Britain's increasing influence. It imposed British rule across countries such as India, Hong Kong, Egypt and Burma. The British Army and British government outposts maintained control, suppressing local populations and meeting disobedience with violence.

The British Empire continued to grow until its peak in 1920, when it ruled almost 24 per cent of the world. It had already begun to weaken, though, due to war: first against Russia and then in World War I. Rebellions and uprisings increased, and the British Empire gradually began to shrink. Over the next 80 years, colonised countries gained their independence, either as a result of unrest or, in some cases, through goodwill.

India gained its independence from Britain on 15 August 1947 after many years of campaigning that was largely led by Mahatma Gandhi. In 1960, Cyprus regained independence, followed by Jamaica and Trinidad in 1961 and 1962. Barbados achieved it in 1966. In only 1997, Hong Kong became a Chinese region once again.

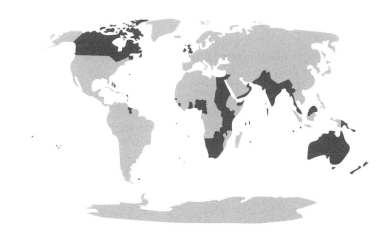

Nowadays, Britain has 14 overseas territories and is also part of the Commonwealth of Nations. This is made up of 53 countries that were almost all once ruled by the British Empire, including India, Canada and Australia. Sixteen of these countries still voluntarily regard the Queen of England as their head of state. Many still have British architecture, legal systems, sports, language and conventions – such as playing cricket, and driving on the left-hand side of the road.

✍ FILL IN THE GAP

Read the sentences and choose the correct word or words to fill the gap. Refer back to
The British Empire **to find the correct answer.**

In total, 13 _____ were established in North America – but by 1770 the
relationship between the colonies and Britain had broken down.

During the 1800s, the British East India Company, which specialised in the trade of tea, cotton, silk, salt
and spices, was used to drive Britain's increasing _____.

After losing control of the _____, Britain further explored Asia and Australia.

🔗 MATCHING

Draw a line with a ruler to match the information.

Captain James Cook	•	•	created in Canada
British East India Company	•	•	covered over six times more land than the Roman Empire
British Empire	•	•	claimed Australia for Britain
Hudson's Bay Company	•	•	drove Britain's influence

🏷 LABEL

Label the description with the correct year.

Cyprus regained independence	
British Empire peaked	
Hudson's Bay Company created	
United States was formed	
Captain Cook claimed Australia for Britain	
slavery made illegal in Britain	

✅ TRUE OR FALSE

Read the sentences. Put a tick in the correct box to show which sentences are *true* and which are *false*.

Hong Kong became a Chinese region in 1997.   True ☐   False ☐

At its peak, Britain ruled almost 24 per cent of the world.   True ☐   False ☐

The British Empire began between the 15th and 17th centuries.   True ☐   False ☐

Conditions in 1770s Australia were excellent.   True ☐   False ☐

The British Army and British government suppressed local populations.   True ☐   False ☐

◎ MULTIPLE CHOICE

Circle the correct answer to the following question.

How many slaves did the British Empire transport across the Atlantic Ocean?

| over 1.7 million | over 2.3 million | over 3.1 million | over 3.5 million |

🔢 SEQUENCING

Look at *The British Empire*. Number the statements from 1 to 4 to show the order they occur in the text.

Nowadays, Britain has 14 overseas territories and is also part of the Commonwealth of Nations.	
In 1607, Britain planned to establish trading and stock companies to manage colonisation attempts in North America.	
In total, 13 British colonies were established in North America – but by 1770 the relationship between the colonies and Britain had broken down.	
Between the late 16th and 18th centuries, Britain expanded its trade network across the world.	

🔍 FIND AND COPY

These questions are about *The British Empire*.

Look at the paragraph beginning 'After losing control of the United States…'. Find and copy a word that tells us that Australia helped make Britain lots of money.

_____

Look at the paragraph beginning 'Nowadays, Britain has 14 overseas territories…'. Find and copy a word that suggests that some countries regard the Queen as their head of state by choice.

_____

🖊 UNDERLINE OR HIGHLIGHT

Read the paragraph below and then follow the instructions.

> In 1960, Cyprus regained independence, followed by Jamaica and Trinidad in 1961 and 1962. Barbados achieved it in 1966. In only 1997, Hong Kong became a Chinese region once again.

Underline or highlight a word that means to get something back which you had lost.

Underline or highlight a word that means to succeed in doing something.

Kangaroos, beaches, barbecues – there are lots of stereotyped images associated with Australia! There's a lot more you may not know about Australia, though: its geography, people and culture.

Australia is the sixth largest country in the world. It's home to more than 20 million people, and has a varied and fascinating culture.

Geography

The climates in Australia are diverse. More than a third of the country is hot desert – this wide, almost unpopulated space is called the 'outback'. Here, temperatures can be extremely high and there is little water or vegetation. Towards the country's south, though, the climate is more accommodating and the land is fertile. There you will find most Australian cities and farms.

Contrary to popular belief, Sydney is not the capital city of Australia – although it does attract the majority of visitors due to its tourist attractions, including its iconic Opera House. Canberra, with a population of nearly 400,000, is the country's capital.

Visitors to Australia also marvel at many of the country's natural features. Uluru (also known as Ayers Rock) is one of its most impressive landmarks. This sacred natural formation stands at around 350 metres tall. It can be found in the Uluru-Kata Tjuta National Park, in the centre of the country and the outback.

Perhaps the most impressive natural wonder, however, is the Great Barrier Reef. This reef – the largest coral reef in the world – is larger than the Great Wall of China. It comprises over 3,000 individual reef systems. Visitors can scuba dive or snorkel to find an abundance of marvellous marine life.

Inhabitants

Australia is home to around 25 million people – five times more than its neighbour, New Zealand. The most populated city in the country is Sydney, which is home to over 4.5 million people. Melbourne follows closely behind: it's home to more than 4 million residents, making even this city ten times bigger than Canberra.

Australia is also home to a diverse range of animals. Due to its remote location, a number of them are not found elsewhere, koalas, kangaroos and platypuses among them. This may be a good thing though, as some of the most dangerous creatures in the world live there too: 36 species of poisonous funnel-web spiders, and 20 different kinds of venomous snakes.

History

Australia's Aboriginal people are believed to have populated the country for at least 50,000 years. They lived in hundreds of different clans, each with a spiritual connection to their land.

Dutch explorers landed in Australia in 1606 and then, in 1770, a British explorer named Captain James Cook claimed Australia for Britain. Colonies and farms were built, but conditions were harsh. Seventeen years later, Britain decided to populate Australia by sending convicted British criminals to serve their sentences there. These new arrivals on the island destroyed the lives of many Aboriginal people, stealing their land and uprooting their lifestyles.

Over the years, soldiers, officers and freed convicts began to build more farms in Australia. More people later moved there in search of cheap land and new opportunities. When gold was found in New South Wales and Victoria, thousands of hopeful people from around the world headed to the island in search of riches. Many of them decided not to return to their homelands and settled in Australia.

In 1901, Australia's six states became a single nation. Despite this, Australia retains diverse cultures, peoples, religions and languages. It is thought that people originally from more than 200 countries call Australia home, and that over 300 languages are spoken. Nearly a quarter of all those living in Australia were born in other countries.

✏️ FILL IN THE GAP

Read the sentences and choose the correct word or words to fill the gap. Refer back to *Australia* to find the correct answer.

Contrary to popular belief, _____ is not the capital city of Australia – although it does attract the majority of visitors due to its tourist attractions, including its iconic Opera House.

_____ follows closely behind: it's home to more than 4 million residents, making even this city ten times bigger than Canberra.

When gold was found in _____ and Victoria, thousands of hopeful people from around the world headed to the island in search of riches.

🔗 MATCHING

Draw a line with a ruler to match the information.

koalas, kangaroos and platypuses	•	•	geography
Dutch explorers landed in 1606	•	•	inhabitants
Uluru	•	•	history
beaches and barbecues	•	•	Australian stereotypes

🏷️ LABEL

Label the description with the correct information.

the largest coral reef in the world	
the year Australia's six states became one	
number of species of poisonous funnel-web spider	
ten times bigger than Canberra	
the capital city of Australia	
metal found in New South Wales and Victoria	

✔️ TRUE OR FALSE

Read the sentences. Put a tick in the correct box to show which sentences are *true* and which are *false*.

Over 300 languages are spoken in Australia. True ☐ False ☐

Captain James Cook claimed Australia for the Dutch in 1606. True ☐ False ☐

Aboriginal people have inhabited Australia for at least 50,000 years. True ☐ False ☐

Australia is the fifth largest country in the world. True ☐ False ☐

More than a third of the country is hot desert. True ☐ False ☐

◎ MULTIPLE CHOICE

Circle the correct answer to the following question.

What is the capital city of Australia?

Canberra	Sydney	Melbourne	New South Wales

123 SEQUENCING

Look at *Australia*. Number the statements from 1 to 4 to show the order they occur in the text.

It can be found in the Uluru-Kata Tjuta National Park, in the centre of the country and the outback.	
It's home to more than 20 million people, and has a varied and fascinating culture.	
This may be a good thing though, as some of the most dangerous creatures in the world live there too: 36 species of poisonous funnel-web spiders, and 20 different kinds of venomous snakes.	
The most populated city in the country is Sydney, which is home to over 4.5 million people.	

🔍 FIND AND COPY

These questions are about *Australia*.

Look at the 'Inhabitants' section. Find and copy a word that suggests that a large number of human beings live in Sydney.

_____

Look at the 'History' section. Find and copy a word that suggests that people decided to live in Australia rather than returning home.

_____

✏ UNDERLINE OR HIGHLIGHT

Read the paragraph below and then follow the instructions.

> Australia is also home to a diverse range of animals. Due to its remote location, a number of them are not found elsewhere, koalas, kangaroos and platypuses among them. This may be a good thing, though, as some of the most dangerous creatures in the world live there, too: 36 species of poisonous funnel-web spiders, and 20 different kinds of venomous snakes.

Underline or highlight a word that means made up of a wide variety.

Underline or highlight a word that means far away and difficult to get to.

Who is Banksy?

Banksy is a street artist whose identity remains unknown. He rose to prominence in the late 1990s for stencilled pieces of graffiti that are intended to make a political or social point.

You may have seen images of Banksy's graffiti art. One of his most famous stencils is 'Girl with Balloon', which shows a young girl letting go of a heart-shaped balloon. Many see it as a reflection of children's loss of innocence and people's lack of respect for love.

Banksy furthered his reputation when he tricked everybody at a London art auction. In 2018, a framed copy of 'Girl with Balloon' was sold for £1 million to an

anonymous phone bidder. Seconds afterwards, a mechanism hidden in its frame shredded it! The shredding stopped half way through the image, leaving half of it whole and half in strips. This piece of art was given a new name: 'Love is in the Bin' – and it's believed to be worth at least 50 per cent more now than when it was undamaged.

Art or vandalism?

Despite the prices paid for his work, many people believe Banksy's art is simple criminal damage because graffiti is illegal. Many also suggest that allowing it to remain in public spaces sets a bad example for other graffiti artists. Some simply think that his comments aren't effective.

Banksy facts – or are they?

Some information about Banksy can be worked out from his art and some details have been given in interviews.

1. Banksy was born in Bristol in 1974, and was the son of a photocopier engineer.

2. When he started creating graffiti art, he was part of the DryBreadZ Crew, a Bristol-based gang.

3. At that point, his work was mainly done freehand. It was only in the late 1990s that his use of stencils in his work developed. They allow complex images to be created quickly – which is important when they're a crime!

4. Banksy says his work was inspired by 3D, a member of the band Massive Attack.

5. He is often compared to French masters of street art, Blek le Rat and Jef Aerosol – but some say he stole their ideas.

6. Banksy has compiled a book called *Wall and Piece*. It contains images of his works, and also some of his thoughts and ideas.

7. He paid an odd tribute to Monet's 'Water Lilies' by adding an old shopping trolley and rubbish to the painting.

8. Banksy does not sell his work through commercial art galleries.

9. In 2004, he printed spoof £10 notes. The Queen was replaced by Princess Diana's face and they said 'Banksy of England' instead of 'Bank of England'.

10. In 2007, Banksy won the 'Greatest Living Briton – The Arts' prize. Naturally, he didn't collect the prize in person.

People have used these clues to come up with theories about who Banksy really is. The person most commonly believed to be Banksy is Robin Gunningham, an artist who was born in Bristol in 1973. Pictures never show Banksy's face but some contain other details that people believe resemble him. Gunningham also moved to London around 2000, which is when Banksy's artwork started appearing there.

Some of Banksy's work and where to find it – if you can!

- 'Season's Greetings': side of two garages, Port Talbot, Wales

- 'The Mild, Mild West': side of a building, Stokes Croft, Bristol

- 'Rage, Flower Thrower': side of a garage, Bethlehem, Palestine

- 'The Grim Reaper': side of a moored boat, Bristol

- 'Washing Zebra Stripes': shattered brick wall, Timbuktu, Mali

- 'Gangsta Rat': Moorfield Eye Hospital, London

- 'There is Always Hope': wall of brick steps, South Bank, London

🕐 FILL IN THE GAP

Read the sentences and choose the correct word or words to fill the gap. Refer back to *Banksy* to find the correct answer.

One of his most famous stencils is '_____', which shows a young girl letting go of a heart-shaped balloon.

Despite the prices paid for his work, many people believe Banksy's art is simple criminal damage because _____ is illegal.

_____ also moved to London around 2000, which is when Banksy's artwork started appearing there.

🔄 MATCHING

Draw a line with a ruler to match the information.

The Mild, Mild West		London
Gangsta Rat		Bethlehem
Washing Zebra Stripes		Bristol
Rage, Flower Thrower		Timbuktu

🏷 LABEL

Label the description with the correct information.

2018 price of 'Girl with Balloon'	
city Banksy was born in	
year Banksy was born	
name of book Banksy wrote	
year Banksy made spoof £10 notes	
city where 'Gangsta Rat' art is	

✅ TRUE OR FALSE

Read the sentences. Put a tick in the correct box to show which sentences are *true* and which are *false*.

'The Mild, Mild West' is one of his most famous stencils. True ☐ False ☐

Everyone agrees that Banksy's art is a great example for others. True ☐ False ☐

Banksy printed spoof £10 notes in 2004. True ☐ False ☐

Banksy's father worked in a bank. True ☐ False ☐

Many people believe Banksy is Robin Gunningham. True ☐ False ☐

◎ MULTIPLE CHOICE

Circle the correct answer to the following question.

What is the title of the Banksy art piece that can be found on the side of a moored boat?

| Season's Greetings | Rage, Flower Thrower | Gangsta Rat | The Grim Reaper |

🔢 SEQUENCING

Look at *Banksy*. Number the statements from 1 to 4 to show the order they occur in the text.

Many see it as a reflection of children's loss of innocence and people's lack of respect for love.	
Seconds afterwards, a mechanism hidden in its frame shredded it!	
This piece of art was given a new name: 'Love is in the Bin' – and it's believed to be worth at least 50 per cent more now than when it was undamaged.	
The Queen was replaced by Princess Diana's face and they said 'Banksy of England' instead of 'Bank of England'.	

🔍 FIND AND COPY

These questions are about *Banksy*.

Look at the paragraph beginning 'At that point'. Find and copy a word that suggests Bansky's early work was done without stencils.

_____

Look at the paragraph beginning 'You may have seen images'. Find and copy a word that suggests that people think love is not respected enough.

_____

◑ UNDERLINE OR HIGHLIGHT

Read the paragraph below and then follow the instructions.

People have used these clues to come up with theories about who Banksy really is. The person most commonly believed to be Banksy is Robin Gunningham, an artist who was born in Bristol in 1973. Pictures never show Banksy's face but some contain other details that people believe resemble him.

Underline or highlight a word that means similar to something.

Underline or highlight a word that means ideas that hope to explain a problem.

1. FAIR TRADE

FILL IN THE GAP

1. discrimination
2. treated
3. developing
4. consequence
5. exploit
6. producers
7. businesses
8. clean
9. coffea
10. Kaldi
11. Monasteries
12. climate
13. 80 per cent
14. millions
15. fair trade

MATCHING

Fair trade focusses on	'developing' countries
Numbers of certified producers	1,411
Goat herder	Kaldi
Close to the equator	coffee belt
Farmers don't have enough	money
Large companies	exploit farmers
Coffee growing region	the coffee belt
Fair trade ensures	everyone treated the same
Paid to fair trade producers	$158.3 million
Fairtrade Foundation logo	guarantee the producer has been paid a fair price
Coffee	a very popular drink
Coffea	a tree
Trade means	buying and selling goods
Fairtrade Foundation logo	green, black and blue
Fair means	equal and without discrimination
Fair trade countries	73
1.66 million	fair trade certified farmers and workers
Energetic goats ate	coffea berries
Small farms produce	80 percent of the world's coffee
Farmers use money for	Clothes, food and medicines

MULTIPLE CHOICE

everyone is treated the same
buying and selling goods
India, Indonesia, Africa and South America
a berry
exploited
producers
powder or granules
coffea
the coffee belt
a circle

TRUE OR FALSE

1. True
2. True
3. False
4. False
5. False
6. True
7. True
8. False
9. True
10. False
11. True
12. False
13. True
14. False
15. True
16. False
17. False
18. True
19. False
20. False

2. EUROPEAN CULTURE

FILL IN THE GAP

1. continent
2. traditions
3. architecture
4. Kurdish
5. classical musicians
6. Ludwig van Beethoven
7. Sport
8. world-famous
9. Vikings
10. government
11. Danes'
12. mythical
13. sun-ripened
14. Colosseum

MATCHING

German culture	Polish, Kurdish and Danish languages
Danish culture	Viking links
Greek culture	Zeus and Hades
Europe	a continent
Greek culture	Trojan War
Danish culture	arts, theatre and culture
German culture	classical musicians
the Parthenon	Greece
olive oil	Greek culture
cycling	Danish culture
motor sports	German culture
Houses of Parliament	London
Danish culture	government funding for the arts
Greek culture	Mediterranean sea
German culture	Beethoven and Bach
symbol of culture	the Colosseum, Rome
Theseus	Minotaur
Paris	the Louvre
royal family	London
exported food	sausages

MULTIPLE CHOICE

over 40
1954
German
Danish
11
USA
Colosseum
Greek
Danish
German

TRUE OR FALSE

1. False
2. True
3. False
4. True
5. True
6. False
7. False
8. True
9. True
10. False
11. False
12. True
13. True
14. False
15. True

FIND AND COPY

divided
recognisable
composed / composers
exported
annual
raided
guarded
illustrates

UNDERLINE OR HIGHLIGHT

official
delicious
celebrated
native
exported
musician

3. PLANETS IN THE SOLAR SYSTEM

FILL IN THE GAP

eight
explored
moon
closest
acidic
opposite
orbit
iron
ten
spacecraft
62
the Sun
Neptune
discovery
properties

MATCHING

Mercury	closest to the sun
Earth	fifth largest planet
Mars	iron
Saturn	hydrogen and helium
Venus	hottest planet
Jupiter	largest planet
Uranus	four times wider than Earth
Neptune	not visible to the naked eye
discovered 1846	Neptune
red planet	Mars
79 moons in total	Jupiter
62 moons in total	Saturn
destroy any vehicle	Jupiter
165 years to orbit the Sun	Neptune
smallest planet	Mercury
spins in opposite direction to Earth	Venus
Earth	365 days to orbit the Sun
Solar system	eight planets
Mercury	88 Earth days to orbit the Sun
Saturn	rings of ice and rock

LABEL

1. Mercury
2. Jupiter
3. Mars
4. Jupiter / Saturn
5. Neptune
6. Uranus
7. Uranus
8. Saturn
9. Mars
10. Earth
11. Mars
12. Saturn
13. Jupiter
14. Venus
15. Neptune
16. Neptune
17. Uranus
18. Saturn

SEQUENCING

2, 3, 4, 1, 5
5, 1, 4, 3, 2
1, 5, 3, 2, 4

FIND AND COPY

scientists / experts
rotation
unusually
inhabited
extinct
similar
uniquely
properties

UNDERLINE OR HIGHLIGHT

feature
completed
distant
support
believed
rotation

4. MENTAL HEALTH

LABEL

1. anxiety
2. OCD / Obsessive-compulsive disorder
3. depression
4. anorexia / bulimia
5. anxiety
6. eating disorders
7. 74 (per cent)
8. endorphins
9. Mind
10. exercising
11. (vitamin) D
12. plants and animals
13. anxiety
14. mental health problems
15. OCD / Obsessive-compulsive disorder
16. eating disorders
17. depression
18. OCD / Obsessive-compulsive disorder

SEQUENCING

2, 3, 1, 4, 5
5, 1, 2, 3, 4
1, 2, 3, 4, 5

MULTIPLE CHOICE

21st century
anxiety
depression
bulimia
2018
doctors
exercise
sun
Mind
OCD

TRUE OR FALSE

1. True
2. True
3. True
4. False
5. True
6. False
7. False
8. False
9. True
10. False
11. True
12. True
13. True
14. False
15. True

FIND AND COPY

cope
significant
inherited
overwhelmed
nervous
persistent
avoid
relentlessly / repeating

UNDERLINE OR HIGHLIGHT

associated / related
reported
logical
disorders
panic
prolonged

5. THE BRITISH EMPIRE

FILL IN THE GAP

British colonies
influence
United States

MATCHING

Captain James Cook	claimed Australia for Britain
British East India Company	drove Britain's influence
British Empire	covered over six times more land than the Roman Empire
Hudson's Bay Company	created in Canada

LABEL

1960
1920
1670
1776
1770
1807

TRUE OR FALSE

1. True
2. True
3. False
4. False
5. True

MULTIPLE CHOICE

over 3.5 million

SEQUENCING

4, 2, 3, 1

FIND AND COPY

profitable
voluntarily

UNDERLINE OR HIGHLIGHT

regained
achieved

6. COUNTRY STUDY: AUSTRALIA

FILL IN THE GAP

Sydney
Melbourne
New South Wales

MATCHING

koalas, kangaroos and platypuses	inhabitants
Dutch explorers landed in 1606	history
Uluru	geography
beaches and barbecues	Australian stereotypes

LABEL

Great Barrier Reef
1901
36
Melbourne
Canberra
gold

TRUE OR FALSE

1. True
2. False
3. True
4. False
5. True

MULTIPLE CHOICE

Canberra

SEQUENCING

2, 1, 4, 3

FIND AND COPY

populated
settled

UNDERLINE OR HIGHLIGHT

diverse / range
remote

7. BANKSY

FILL IN THE GAP

Girl with Balloon
graffiti
Gunningham

MATCHING

The Mild, Milk West	Bristol
Gangsta Rat	London
Washing Zebra Stripes	Timbuktu
Rage, Flower Thrower	Bethlehem

LABEL

£1 million
Bristol
1974
Wall and Piece
2004
London

TRUE OR FALSE

1. False
2. False
3. True
4. False
5. True

MULTIPLE CHOICE

The Grim Reaper

SEQUENCING

1, 2, 3, 4

FIND AND COPY

freehand
lack

UNDERLINE OR HIGHLIGHT

resemble
theories